IT WILL BE OKAY

WRITTEN & ILLUSTRATED BY

VLADIMIR SAINTE

ISBN-13: 978-1-942005-52-0

Content X Design, Inc.
PO Box 8754, Kansas City, MO 64114

DEAR READERS,

AS HEALTHY ROLE MODELS FOR THE CHILDREN WE CARE FOR, IT'S OUR RESPONSIBILITY TO INSPIRE THEIR HOPES AND DREAMS. FEAR OFTEN KEEPS US FROM TRYING NEW THINGS OR HAVING THE DRIVE TO REACH FOR THE STARS. THERE IS GREAT STRENGTH IN IDENTIFYING FEAR, DEFINING ITS ORIGIN, AND FACING IT. WE HAVE THE CAPABILITY FOR SO MUCH MORE AND SHOULD DO OUR BEST TO REMEMBER THAT IT'S OKAY TO FAIL. FAILING GIVES US THE OPPORTUNITY TO LEARN FROM OUR MISTAKES AND TRY AGAIN.

REMEMBER, WHEN WE TREAT EACH OTHER (AND OURSELVES) WITH DIGNITY AND RESPECT, IT HELPS THE WORLD TURN A LITTLE EASIER. EVERYONE HAS THE POTENTIAL FOR GREATNESS — IT JUST TAKES A LITTLE LOVE, NURTURING SUPPORT, AND SEEING YOURSELF AS A HERO.

THIS IS ALMA AND HER MOM.
ALMA USED TO BE HAPPY,
BUT LATELY, SHE'S BEEN
FEELING SAD.
HER PARENTS ARE NO LONGER
TOGETHER AND SHE'S
BEING BULLIED AT SCHOOL.
SHE FEELS ALONE A LOT.
BUT WHAT ALMA DOESN'T
KNOW YET IS SHE HAS
SUPERPOWERS.

SHE USED TO ENJOY
READING COMIC BOOKS,
LISTENING TO MUSIC,
AND GOING OUTSIDE
TO PLAY WITH HER FRIENDS.

SHE WOULD LIKE TO DO
THOSE THINGS AGAIN,
BUT CERTAIN FEELINGS
ARE GETTING IN HER WAY.

THIS IS LIMBO,
THE FEAR MONSTER.

HE USES HIS SCARY POWERS
TO MAKE ALMA FEEL
FRIGHTENED AND SAD.

SOMETIMES ALMA FEELS
NERVOUS, WORRIED,
AND STUCK.

SHE SHOWS THESE FEELINGS
IN DIFFERENT WAYS.

THIS MAKES LIMBO VERY HAPPY.

SOMETIMES ALMA FEELS LONELY AND HAS A HARD TIME BEING AWAY FROM HER MOM.

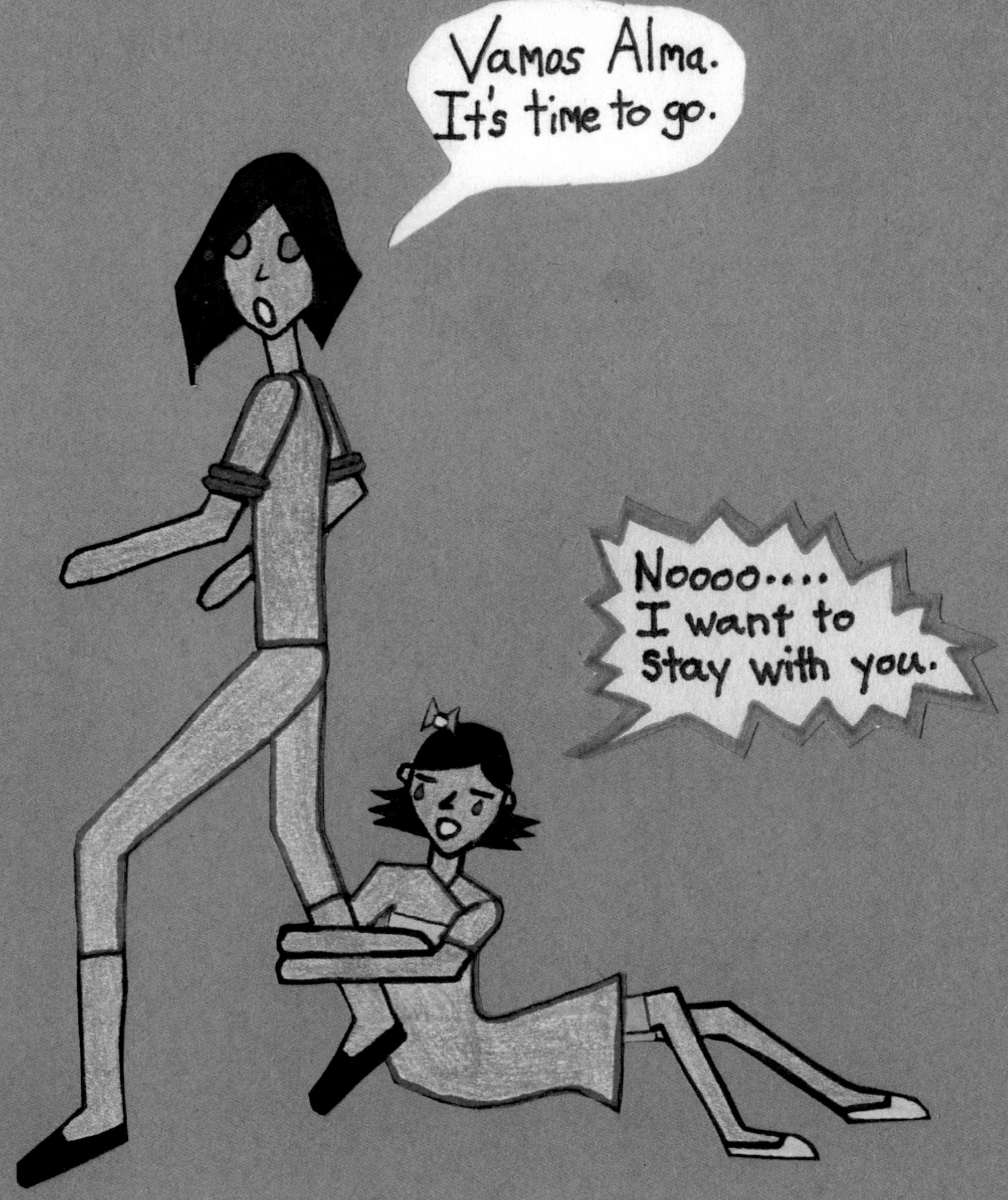
Vamos Alma. It's time to go.
Noooo.... I want to stay with you.

ONE TIME ALMA RAISED HER HAND TO ANSWER A QUESTION IN CLASS AND WAS BULLIED FOR NO REASON.

HER FRIENDS TRIED TO MAKE HER FEEL BETTER, BUT SHE WAS AFRAID TO RAISE HER HAND AGAIN.

ALMA'S WORRIED FEELINGS
BECAME SO BIG
THAT HER MOM
BROUGHT HER TO SEE
A THERAPIST NAMED MR. DAVE.

MR. DAVE AND ALMA WORKED TOGETHER AND TALKED ABOUT ALL OF THE THINGS THAT WERE MAKING HER UPSET.

IT TOOK SOME TIME, BUT EVENTUALLY SHE GOT MORE COMFORTABLE TALKING ABOUT HER FEELINGS.

WHEN ALMA WAS READY, MR. DAVE
SHOWED HER THE *HOPE* SHIELD,
WHICH WAS THE SOURCE OF HER
POWERS.

THE SHIELD HELPED REMIND HER
OF ALL THE THINGS SHE HAD
LEARNED IN THERAPY.

WITH THE HELP OF HER *HOPE* SHIELD, SHE WAS ABLE TO PRACTICE HER NEW SKILLS EVERY DAY AND NIGHT UNTIL SHE WAS READY TO BATTLE LIMBO.

Taking a break

Deep breaths

Getting exercise

SHE FOUND THE HERO
THAT WAS BURIED
UNDERNEATH HER WORRIES.

SHE NO LONGER ALLOWED HER FEARS TO KEEP HER FROM RAISING HER HAND IN CLASS.

SHE KNEW IT WAS OKAY TO TRY.

LIMBO DID NOT LIKE ALMA FEELING
CONFIDENT AND *STRONG*.

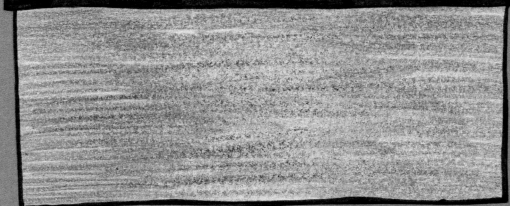

BUT ALMA WAS NO LONGER AFRAID
AND USED HER *HOPE* SHIELD
TO BANISH LIMBO
BACK TO FEAR ISLAND.

AFTER DEFEATING LIMBO AND
FEELING STRONG,
ALMA USED HER *HOPE* SHIELD TO
HELP HER FRIENDS
BATTLE THEIR FEAR MONSTERS.

AND THEN THEY WERE READY TO
TAKE ON THE WORLD.

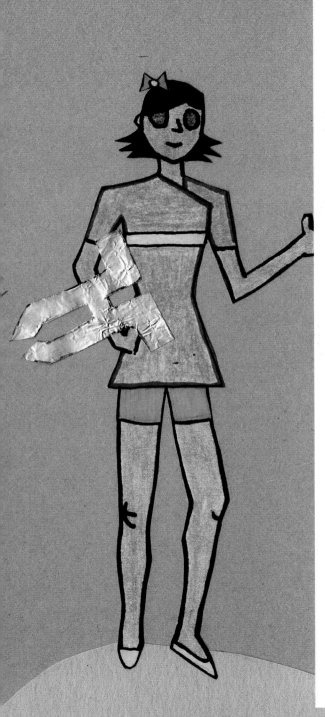

POWERS/SKILLS

BELOW ARE ALMA'S SUPERPOWERS. EACH OF THE ABILITIES INCLUDES HEALTHY ACTIVITIES TO PROMOTE A POSITIVE SELF-IMAGE, REDUCE ANXIETY, AND ENHANCE CONNECTION. THE PRIMARY GOALS ARE TO CREATE A POSITIVE INTERACTION WHILE READING THIS BOOK WITH A CHILD AND TO HELP THEM UNDERSTAND THAT FEAR IS A VALID AND NATURAL FEELING. AS CAREGIVERS, IT IS IMPORTANT TO EDUCATE OURSELVES ON HOW FEARS AND ANXIETIES ARE A PART OF NORMAL CHILDHOOD DEVELOPMENT.

NOTE: CHILDREN ARE NATURALLY RESILIENT, AND WHEN PROPERLY SUPPORTED, THEY CAN COPE WITH NUMEROUS ADVERSITIES AND PROBLEMS, AND ADJUST TO THEIR ENVIRONMENT.

- INTUITIVE REACTION: ABILITY TO USE LEARNED SKILLS (I.E., RELAXATION, DEEP BREATHING, REDUCING NEGATIVE THOUGHTS) TO ADDRESS GROWING FEARS AND WORRIES.

- PREDICTIVE FORESIGHT: ABILITY TO PREDICT POTENTIALLY ANXIOUS SITUATIONS (I.E., TAKING A TEST, GIVING A PRESENTATION, ETC.) IN ORDER TO USE EFFECTIVE COPING SKILLS IN PREPARATION.

- ALLIANCE ENHANCEMENT: ABILITY TO BUILD POSITIVE AND CONNECTED RELATIONSHIPS WITH PEOPLE WHO BELIEVE IN THEM.

ON THE PICTURE BELOW, YOU CAN COLOR, WRITE, OR DRAW WHAT YOU FEEL INSIDE WHEN YOU'RE ANXIOUS, WORRIED, OR SCARED LIKE ALMA.

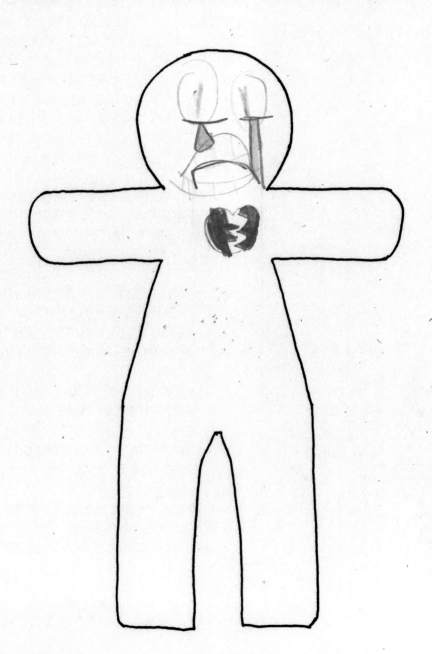

WHAT DOES YOUR FEAR MONSTER LOOK LIKE?

WHAT ARE THREE THINGS YOU CAN DO TO SCARE YOUR FEAR MONSTER AWAY?

CUT OUT YOUR **HOPE** SHIELD & CARRY IT WITH YOU LIKE ALMA.

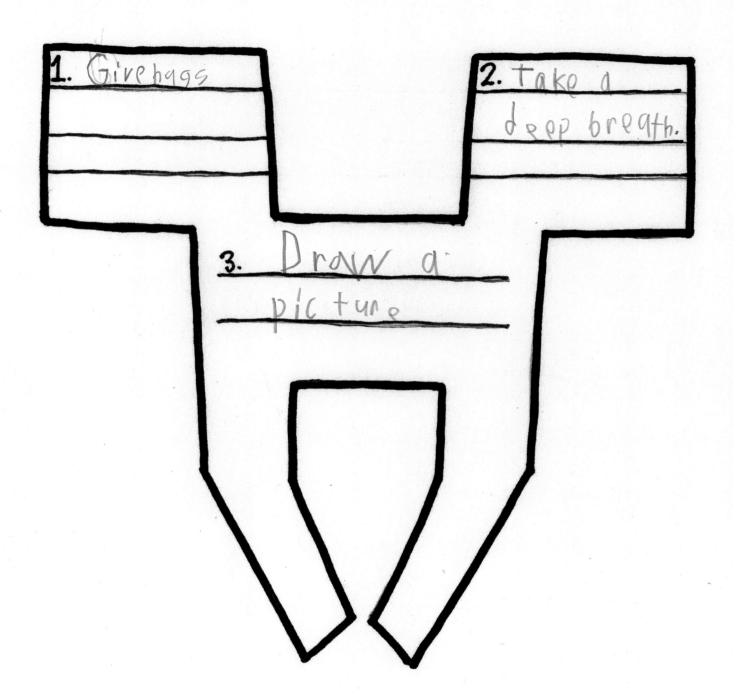

1. Give hugs

2. Take a deep breath.

3. Draw a picture

WITH MORE THAN TEN YEARS' EXPERIENCE AS A THERAPIST, VLADIMIR SAINTE, LCSW HAS MADE AN INVALUABLE IMPACT ON THE KANSAS CITY COMMUNITY THROUGH HIS WORK AS A COUNSELOR AND CRISIS CLINICIAN.

SAINTE IS COMMITTED TO PROVIDING SUPPORTIVE COUNSELING, NOT JUST WITH CHILDREN, BUT THROUGH A PARTNERSHIP WITH THEIR FAMILIES AND THE BROADER COMMUNITY MEMBERS FOR A HOLISTIC IMPACT ON THE CHILD'S DEVELOPMENT.

SAINTE GRADUATED WITH A BACHELOR OF ARTS IN SOCIOLOGY AND A MASTER OF SOCIAL WORK FROM THE UNIVERSITY OF MISSOURI-KANSAS CITY.

A COMPLETE LIST OF ALL VLADIMIR'S TITLES AND MORE INFORMATION CAN BE FOUND AT: VLADIMIRSAINTE.COM

FOLLOW HIM ON INSTAGRAM AT VLA1899.

ALSO BY VLADIMIR SAINTE:
JUST LIKE A HERO

Made in the USA
Monee, IL
16 February 2020